Jen has a pet.
Jen's pet is Max.

2

Max is not well.
Jen pets Max.

Jen puts Max in a box.
The box is big.

3

4 Dad put the box and Max in the van.
Dad and Jen go to the vet.

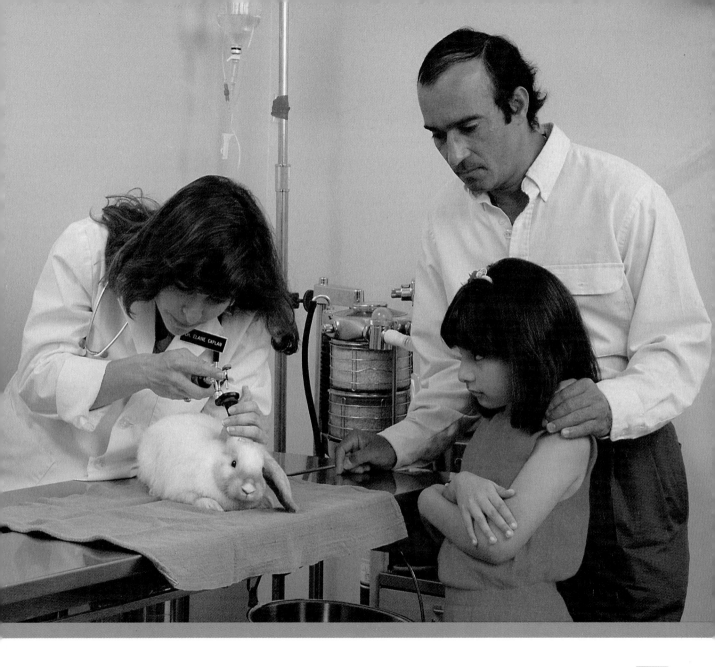

Jen tells the vet, "Max is not well."
The vet tells Jen, "I will fix Max."

5

6

The vet tells Jen, "Max will get well."
The vet puts Max in the box.

Dad, Jen, and Max get in the van.

8

Max is well.
Jen and Max have fun.